The Car

by the same author
MEN IN WHITE COATS

in preparation
SPORT
STUFFING

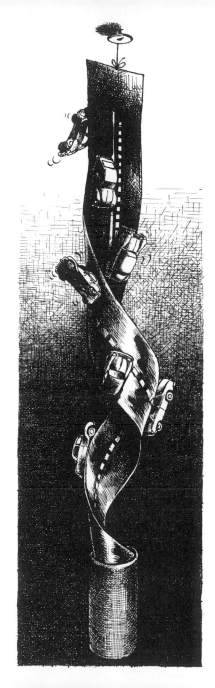

Claude Serre

The Car

Methuen

First published in Great Britain in 1984
by Methuen London Ltd
11 New Fetter Lane, London EC4P 4EE
Copyright © 1978 by Editions Jacques Glénat
Made and printed in Great Britain

ISBN 0 413 53750 1

Reproduced, printed and bound in Great Britain by
Hazell Watson & Viney Limited,
Member of the BPCC Group,
Aylesbury, Bucks

1

2

3

4

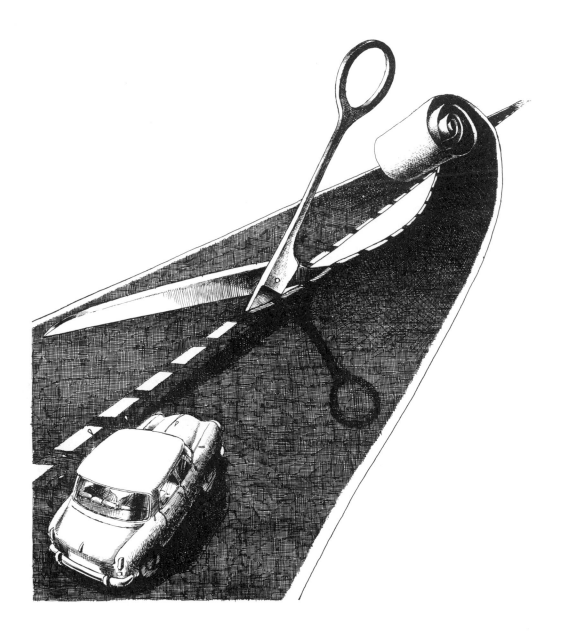

was my right of way!

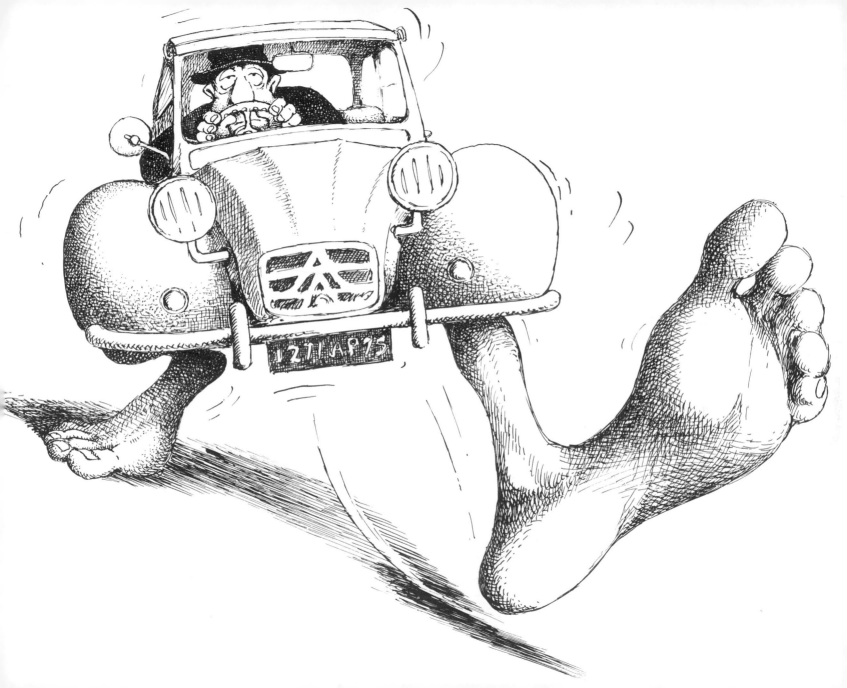

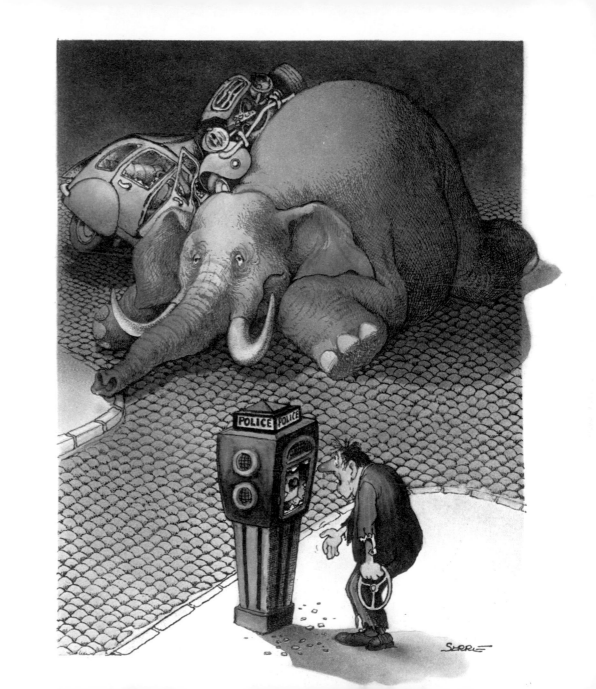

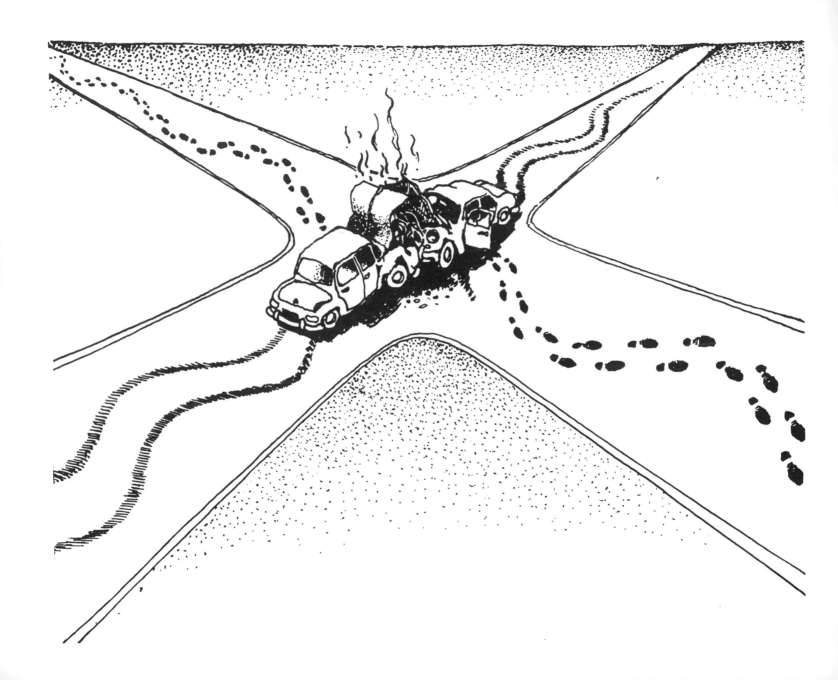

FOG WARNING

SERRE

2041 Q175